# The 1:

# *@©#K-UPS

G000135974

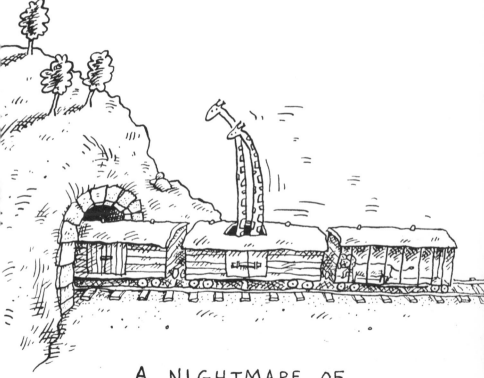

## A NIGHTMARE OF
## INADVERTENT CALAMITIES

## Kjartan Poskitt & Steven Appleby

Published by Grub Street
The Basement, 10 Chivalry Road, London SW11 1HT

A catalogue record of this title is available from the British Library

ISBN 1 898697 11 6

Printed and bound by Biddles Ltd, Guildford and King's Lynn

THE SLOPING
ROOF GARDEN.

MR AND MRS PATTERSON
FORGET TO SET THE
BURGLAR ALARM.

CAPITANO SPITZERO
WANTS A GOOD VIEW.

THE MOON STOPS FOR A REST.

THE SELLOTAPE FACTORY FORGETS TO
PUT ENDS ON THE ROLLS.

1 - DOCTOR JOHNSON GETS OFF TO
   A BAD START.

## 2 - DOCTOR JOHNSON GETS DEPRESSED...

## 3 - DOCTOR JOHNSON FINALLY GETS ANOTHER IDEA.

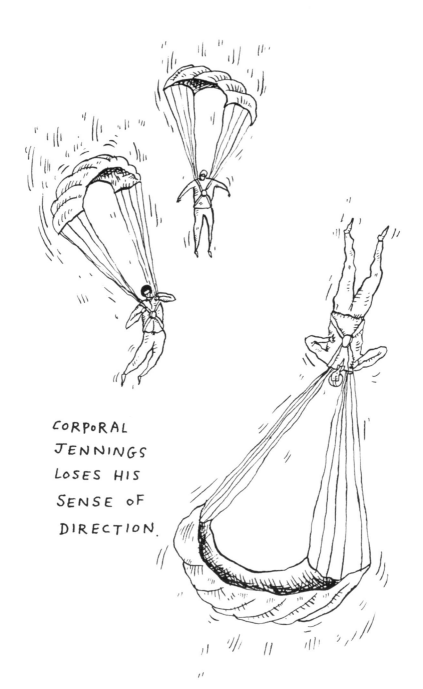

CORPORAL
JENNINGS
LOSES HIS
SENSE OF
DIRECTION.

NELSON'S LAST WORDS ARE
MISUNDERSTOOD.

THE EVERLASTING
7-YEAR LYCRA NAPPY...

AND THE

SUPER-ABSORBENT NAPPY.

# GREAT EXPLORERS no. 1:

SIR EDMUND HILARY
CONQUERS THE
WRONG MOUNTAIN.

SANTA OVERDOES
THE MINCE PIES.

CLUNK!

ARNOLD PUTS UP A NOTICE.

THE STAR TREK CONVENTION INVITE A
REAL KLINGON TO BE GUEST OF HONOUR.

ALADDIN CAN'T WAIT TO TRY OUT HIS NEW LAMP.

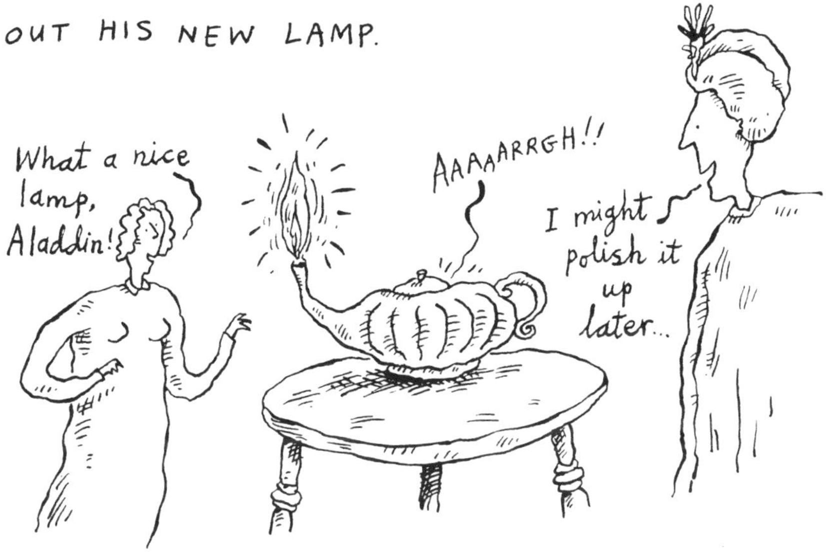

ROO BRINGS
A FRIEND
TO TEA.

NELSON INVITES
NAPOLEON TO A
ROWING
COMPETITION.

NAVIGATOR GIBSON PLANS A
BAD SHORT CUT.

EVERYONE UNDERESTIMATES THE
RESOURCEFULNESS OF THE VENUS FLYTRAP.

# THE MOBILE TELEPHONE TAKES ADVANTAGE OF INOPPORTUNE OPPORTUNITIES:

i -

ii -

iii ~

iv ~

LONG JOHN SILVER'S PARROT UTTERS
ITS LAST WORDS.

HERBERT OPENED
THE SEED PACKET
AT THE WRONG
END.

Watch out for
King Leer!

SHAKESPEARE LOSES HIS SUBTLETY.

A DENTIST FORGETS TO SERVICE
HIS DRILL BIT.

# GULLIBLE VICTIMS OF FASHION EXCESSES:

## ENHANCED BODY PIERCING.

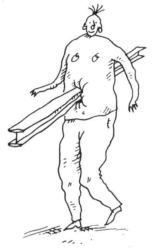

## CLONE COUPLES.

## CULTIVATED BODY HAIR.

## INORDINATE TATTOOING.

FINGERNAIL EXTENTIONS.

CO-ORDINATED PETS.

TOWER PLATFORM SHOES.

NO-ONE REALISED THE ENCYCLOPAEDIA
EDITOR'S PENCHANT FOR HERMIT CRABS.

THE LUNCH ROTA IS MISUNDERSTOOD.

# THE TURBO EXTRACTOR FAN.

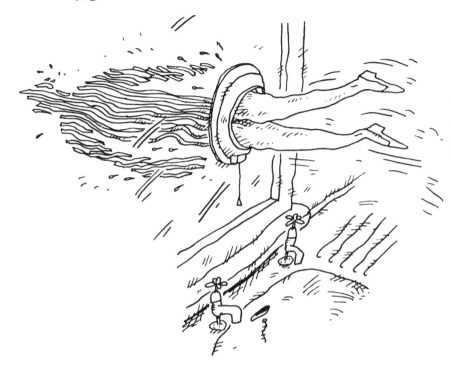

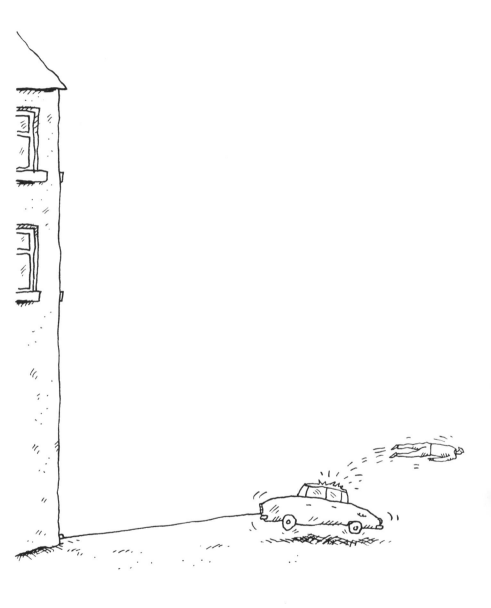

MAINS-POWERED ELECTRIC CAR.

THE INVENTOR OF THE CONDOM
DOESN'T SUCCEED IMMEDIATELY.

THE ANTEATERS EXPERIMENT
WITH FRENCH KISSING

"I BET YOU A TENNER YOU CAN'T"
BRIGADIER ROGERS HAD SCOFFED
AT THE VOODOO DOCTOR.

and I still owe
him the £10.

# CREATION GETS OFF TO A BAD START:

i — ADAM GETS POSSESSIVE.

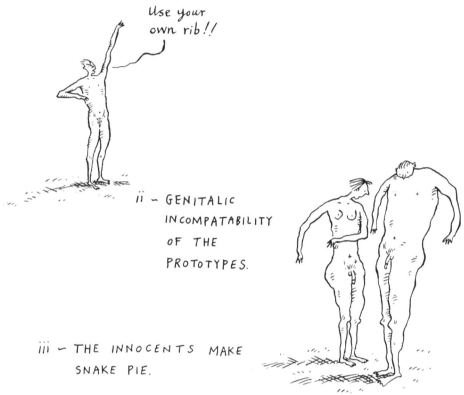

ii — GENITALIC INCOMPATABILITY OF THE PROTOTYPES.

iii — THE INNOCENTS MAKE SNAKE PIE.

## iv ~ ADAM BUILDS A SHED.

## v ~ EVE GETS A BETTER OFFER.

If you'd went before you came then you wouldn't have needed to have gone.

MR BOOMERANG
FAILS TO
BENEFIT
FROM HIS
INVENTION.

GUSTAFF EIFFEL DESIGNS A PYLON.

# DOCTOR ROBINSON FAILS TO LOOK UP.

# A SNAIL PUTS A SHELF UP.

THE POTENTIAL OF THE WHEEL
IS OVERLOOKED.

JAMES BOND CAN'T FIND THE
WINDOW WASHER.

MARIE ANTOINETTE SHOWS OFF
HER MECHANICAL KNOWLEDGE.

CLARK KENT TAKES HIS GLASSES OFF.

GILBERT FALLS IN LOVE.

FRED HADN'T REALISED HIS CAR
WAS DRY-CLEAN ONLY.

THE ESCAPE COMMITTEE
MISCALCULATES.

ALEXANDER GRAHAM BELL'S
GREAT INVENTION.

# PROTOTYPES FOR THE TROJAN HORSE:

## 2 - THE TROJAN GOAT.

b ~

c ~

EMPLOYING
AN HONEST
VICAR.

If anyone here present knows
of any just cause or impediment
why these two persons
should not be joined
together in holy
matrimony, apparently
the bride's father
would offer a
large cash sum
if you were to
declare it.

THE HIGH POWER BIDET.

PAVAROTTI BUNGIE JUMPING.

MOZART'S MOTHER LETS HIM
PLAY FOOTBALL.

NOAH UNDERESTIMATES THE APPETITE
OF THE TWO WOODWORM.

LEONARDO
TELLS THE
WRONG JOKE.

MOSES CAN'T BE BOTHERED
WITH THE SECOND TRIP.

MRS JONES DECIDES THE ELECTRICIAN
NEEDS MORE LIGHT.

THE ANGLO-U.S. FOOTBALL MATCH.

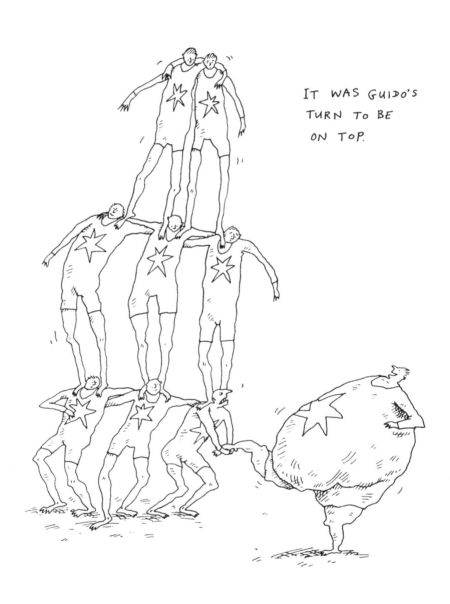

IT WAS GUIDO'S
TURN TO BE
ON TOP.

ONE SMALL STEP FOR MAN, A GIANT
COUP FOR DOG KIND.

THE IMPERIAL ARMY MISUNDERSTAND
THE REQUIREMENTS OF THE GOOSE STEP.

MRS JONES PHONES TO CHECK
ON THE PLUMBER.

THE OXFORD AND CAMBRIDGE
SUBMARINE RACE.

AN EVOLUTIONARY FLOP:

THE CHOCOLATASAURUS.

THE GILLETTE REVOLVING DOOR.

GREAT EXPLORERS no. 2:

Thank God...

CAPTAIN SCOTT THINKS HE'S FOUND HELP.

GEORGE & ALICE
HAD EXPECTED
A LONGER POWER CUT.

But I __AM__ naked!

THE NUDIST
BEACH
INSPECTOR
ACCOSTS
MIKE.

KEVIN'S
BARBEQUE IS
RUNNING LATE.

ISSAC NEWTON ASKS THE
WRONG QUESTION

fig 1:

fig 2:

why do I always get the one with the maggot in it?

IVAN SPLASHSKI FORGETS
TO TURN.

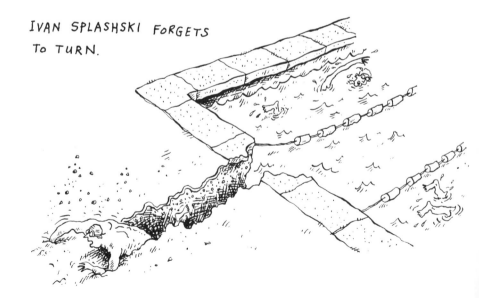

THE TEMPTATION
OF MICKY.

SOMETIME IN THE PAST JIM HAD
LIED ABOUT HIS EYESIGHT.

DORIS TAKES THE WEIGHT OFF HER FEET.

RUBBER DOOR KEYS.

SOLITAIRE HIDE AND SEEK.

BARBEQUED ICE CREAM.

SOLAR POWERED TUBE TRAIN.

GREAT
EXPLORERS no. 3:

COLUMBUS STARTS AN IRRITATING TREND.

BERNARD FAILS TO SNEAK
THROUGH CUSTOMS.

KING CHEOPS OF EGYPT FORGETS TO PUT
A SCALE ON HIS DESIGN FOR SOME NEW
TRAFFIC BOLLARDS.

PICASSO SELECTS THE WRONG MODEL.

MID-OPERATION AMNESIA.

TONY CAN'T
FACE ANOTHER
*G#K-UP.

TWO AUTHORS AND A PUBLISHING
TEAM MISS A CHANCE TO PROMOTE
PREVIOUS BOOKS.